Oswald the Owl

Patrick Garland

Oswald the Owl

WITH ILLUSTRATIONS BY
NICOLA GREEN

SINCLAIR-STEVENSON

This story is dedicated to all my friends
at Chichester Cathedral
and my niece, Amanda Seddon, aged thirteen,
who was the first to hear it.

First published in Great Britain by
Sinclair-Stevenson Limited
7/8 Kendrick Mews
London SW7 3HG, England

British Library Cataloguing in Publication Data
Garland, Patrick
Oswald the owl.
I. Title   II. Green, Nicola
823.914 [J]

ISBN 1-85619-024-2

Photoset by Rowland Phototypesetting Limited
Bury St Edmunds, Suffolk
Printed in England by Clays Ltd, St Ives plc

I

THIS story of Oswald the Owl is so curious that,
although it might have happened long ago, it
is of some surprise to discover it all took place in
very recent memory, at the time of the Great Storm,
and Ralph the Forester told me I should write it
down for you. So here it is. And, what is more, it is
true.

There were three of them, to begin with. Old
Owl, Winston the Urban Fox, and Ratty, who only
said two things: 'Now this *is* a bit of orlright', and
'Nice weather for the time of year'. And they lived
together, far from the eyes of anybody, wanderer,
lost boy, or gamekeeper, deep in the green cathedral of Runcton Woods. Old Owl, by far the
wisest of them, and the oldest too, was an eagle-owl,
with feathery ears which stood up like tall tufts of
grass; he was also their leader, because Winston the
fox, and the rat, all agreed he was wiser than they
were, and had lived longer, and had seen more of
the world. He could hear things from a very great

distance, and was able to sit on the branch of his favourite old tree, with his eyes closed, and know exactly what was going on for miles around. He was able to detect a leaf falling through the air. He also had the disconcerting habit of swivelling his head right round behind him; sometimes he would tilt it sideways, at an angle of ninety degrees to the left, without opening his eyes.

Runcton Woods formed a part of the dense undergrowth and untrodden forest of the Andredswald. In the Dark Ages, when the Roman cities were deserted and in ruins, the ancient walls crumbling and tumbling down, and the cellars of the noble houses inhabited by colonies of rats, the natives cowered in small settlements by the shore. Inland they were isolated by a black and inhospitable forest, the greatest in the whole of England, created, wise old women said, by the devil 'to keep the people trapped within'. The primitive Saxons who lived about its fearful edges even called it 'the undwelt-in-wood'. Although this was not strictly true – the forest was 'undwelt-in' only by men and women. Within its secret foliage the undergrowth teemed with wild creatures – it was the refuge of herds of red deer, wild oxen, grey wolves and fierce boars; beavers and polecats lurked there, so did stone-martens and wild cats; beneath the branches was the Great Bustard, the largest flying bird that ever inhabited this island. Old story-tellers would speak of men out hunting on the Downs, who were attacked and flung off their horses by these savage birds. That is why, Ralph the Forester told me, the nervous inhabitants called the Andredswald 'the terror-wood'.

It was to the protection of these impenetrable green citadels with their wealth of trackless woods, swamp and marsh at their feet, impassable to man or woman, that the Roman Britons fled when the warlike Saxons pursued them, and burned Regnum to the ground. Long before these woodlands gave place to the whale-backed Downs, grazed by the soft mouths of sheep, refreshed by dew-ponds, and dotted with windmills, the Andredswald isolated half of the kingdom of Sussex from the rest of England. To those living beyond its borders it seemed to be its own country, independent, secret, and untrodden. It was known as 'the Wild' for many centuries.

Even to this day, there can still be discovered areas of such concealment, and that is why Old Owl and his little circle of friends lived deep in Runcton Woods. After all, the eagle-owl, for all his magnificence, was a stranger to these shores and besides, even were he not, all owls knew they were the prey of any gamekeeper strolling by, whether it was out of mischief or duty or, worst of all, mere whim. But here, in the hollow of his thorn-tree, Old Owl felt secure. Barely any humans walked under these outspread boughs, and even if they did they never thought of looking above their heads (few people ever do) and not many nocturnal creatures did either; the combination of a fox and an owl close to the same tree-trunk was warning enough. The larger creatures, the timid roe-deer, the restless badger, the spiteful weasel, all enquired from time to time about health, the weather, the prospects for the future, but never interfered with the day-to-day running of things. So Runcton Woods satisfied Old Owl's passion for privacy, and his nostalgia for the ancient past. The only real intruder was Ralph the Forester, and he was not entirely unwelcome, because he had a friendly word for everything which crossed his path, and was often heard humming to himself country tunes which Old Owl so loved, and which sang of the spring and the winter and the changing of the weathers and the passing of time, to say nothing of his many songs of love. For of the three things Old Owl valued the best, remoteness, privacy, the company of friends, there was one thing even more important; most of all, he loved music.

Strangely enough, it was music which brought the three of them together, the owl, the rat, and the urban fox, although their tastes differed wildly. Winston, for example, worked through his day to the unending beat of reggae, hip-hop and rap, while Ratty, who was taciturn for most of the time, greatly preferred music he could nod his head and twitch his tail to. And Old Owl . . . ? Well, he never knew exactly what kind of music he *did* like, as there were beautiful sounds he could hear inside his head, which his long, sensitive ears could never entirely define in everyday life. He could distinguish the church bells of all the different parishes on a Sunday

morning – the tenor bell of St Alban's, Cold Wal-
tham, and Big Walter, from the Bell Tower of the
Cathedral itself. It was frequently his delight to float
up to the very top of the Downs, Windmill Hill,
The Trundle or Thunderbarrow, just to listen to
the haunting sounds the wind made, or the distant
roar of traffic on the motorway, or the lightship out
at Selsey Bill moodily grumbling 'Boring – Boring'
to warn other vessels of sea-fret around the Shoals.
He could imitate the sound of wind far off curling
around the chimney corners, and the marsh-birds
mimicked the music of the sea, or the piercing edge
of the gale; and larks impersonated the summer sigh
the breezes gave as they whispered in the rushes of
Thorney Deeps, or Amberley Wild Brooks. The
natural music of the sky and the sea and the earth
consoled and comforted him, for Old Owl was
frequently of a melancholy disposition rather than
a merry one – when he sat alone on the top of
the world, motionless, and still, listening with his
feathery ear-tufts behind seemingly closed eyes.

Even in the days of long ago, which were not
quite so forgotten in the owl-world as they are in
ours (because owls are always telling things to one
another to keep their memory fresh), Great Bustards
were less scarce than eagle-owls, as the Bustards
inhabited the 'undwelt-in forest', but the eagle-owls
arrived in migrations. Nobody knew for sure where
Old Owl, or his compatriots, ever did come from,
they seemed, as it were, to 'turn up'. Somebody
once said, as far away as the Arctic North, but that

did seem an awfully long way. Old Owl himself was unsure – he claimed to have been brought up in captivity; but there was a story told of the great October moon migration, when an eagle-owl arrived exhausted and wind-blown, and was discovered out on Sidlesham Marsh fast asleep under a sand dune. Clinging to its feathers, trembling like the frail wings of a moth, was the tiniest of all English birds, a goldcrest. It had travelled on the owl's back as a passenger, across the sea, all the way from the Northern Isles.

Old Owl had been brought to England by a traveller, or a librarian, or was it a ticket-of-leave man? He preferred the last explanation, as nobody in the wild was entirely certain what a ticket-of-leave man was. All he remembered was a tiring journey on board ship, leather travelling suitcases, and a large gold cage, extremely imposing and elegant, he recalled, with a domed top to it. His visits to occasional aviaries around the countryside reminded him of his own rather aristocratic prison, like Castle Howard, with handsome porticoes and a Palladian façade. The past tended to blur in his mind and, although he remembered very well the night he escaped from his ornamental cage, he could never quite remember the exact year; one autumn, he thought. He quartered silently thereafter the gardens and deer-park of Wildernesse, that lovely Victorian house reclining in a thousand acres of parkland, and took refuge in a cedar tree which overlooked an old-fashioned rose garden. These

6

gardens he shared with rabbits and roe-deer, hunting the wood-voles and frogs which pottered about at will. He was happy at Wildernesse, and would very likely be living there still, but the old Dowager Duchess died, and the house with its celebrated gardens were sold; and the nice young couple of newly-weds, who were the new proprietors, decided one day to dig out the rose garden to make a swimming-pool. This was no hardship, as Old Owl could only listen to, but never smell, the old-fashioned roses, the Celestial, Maiden's Blush, the Zéphyrine Drouhin, and he withdrew to the seclusion of the venerable cedar-tree where, one evening, he made the acquaintance of an old inarticulate Stage Rat.

No one, throughout his entire life, had thought of giving him a proper name, because he was not really a rat at all, and had never been one; he was a stage-property rat, and he once belonged to an old play-actor, who called him quite simply, and for want of anything more inventive, Ratty. He was made out of very inferior velveteen (cut from the collar of an overcoat once used in melodrama) and he had one black boot-button eye. His skin was stuffed with rifle-shot, so that he tended to *sprawl* rather than squat, legs akimbo, wherever he was set. His tail was his finest point, made from whipcord, and he was proud of the way it curled freely at the tip. In fact, he had been quite famous in his own day, oh, years ago now, in twice-nightly revue. With the play-actor, he had toured the provinces, and he even enjoyed a short engagement in the West End. Ratty had been carried on stage on a tray, alongside rather inferior properties, like toads, bats, and tadpoles, made from india-rubber; but he was always singled out for special attention and acclaim, and held up to the audience: 'Penny for the Ghoul!' the play-actor would cry, and the audience would roar. This experience, 'on the boards' as they say, and the laughter he engendered, Ratty found very pleasing, and he developed quite a taste for theatrical life. But, sadly, it didn't last (things in the theatre seldom do), and both the play-actor and Ratty fell with it, when the fashionable revue itself fell out of favour. He was discarded in an anonymous property-cupboard under the stage, sharing the cramped corner with rubber daggers, wooden flagons, and cardboard bottles.

And it was there, in the props-cupboard, he overheard the only two phrases he ever managed to learn by heart, from the cheerful stage-doorman, who came from Pennyfields, and these were either: 'Now, this *is* a bit of orlright!' Or, 'Nice weather for the time of year!' Both of which Ratty delivered in a broad cockney accent you could cut a loaf of bread with.

One thing led to another, a life in the theatre being nomadic and unpredictable, and the stage-doorman took Ratty home one day and gave him to an odious grandchild, as a cloth-companion. The odious grandchild stuck a knife in his velveteen coat, and some of the rifle-shot trickled out, and he was sent off to a Bring-and-Buy. From there, minus a boot-button, he was shuffled aside to a Car Boot Sale. Someone impertinently tied a knot in his tail. Given away as a Free Gift (and a not-very-popular one at that) in a Church Bazaar, he was abandoned underneath a garden-chair by another odious grand-child, and left to rot in the winter storms.

It was Old Owl, quartering the ivy, who mistook him for a sleek brown field rat, and, thinking of him for supper, transported him away on slow, soundless wings. It was only when he deposited him in the cedar-tree, and Ratty announced improbably, 'Now, this *is* a bit of orlright!' that Owl began to consider the likelihood of error. What began as a nearly disastrous misunderstanding ended in devoted friendship. For what Old Owl really liked about Ratty was his taciturnity. Owl couldn't bear people making a whole lot of unnecessary noise, and he said once that, rather than be spoken to out of turn, he would prefer captivity in a Theme Park.

Perhaps, for other people, this 'gift' of taciturnity was not so very much, but Old Owl seemed to accept it. Nobody could claim that Ratty was an eloquent, or even rudimentary, conversationalist. It was simply no use for sombody to say: 'Good heavens, there's a stunning party at Halnaker, we simply must invite Ratty over . . .', because all he would ever contribute would be 'Nice weather for the time of year', or 'Now this *is* a bit of orlright' – but it was perfectly adequate for Old Owl, who was taciturn by nature. He preferred to listen to sounds other than tittle-tattle, or chitter-chatter, of which, in his view, there was a great deal too much. Starlings and chaffinches, for instance, he could not abide. All waterfowl, and in particular dunlin and godwits, did nothing but gossip, thousands of them, endlessly, for days on end. So, in their quiet way, Old Owl and Ratty had a great deal in common, and wherever one was to go the other would surely follow. Besides, armed with only one eye, half a stomach, a knot in his tail, and very limited conversation, poor Ratty was somewhat underprivileged, and needed a friend.

So, it came about that, when the newly-weds had built the swimming-pool and dug out the old-fashioned rose garden, Ratty and Old Owl retreated into the darker boughs of the ancient cedar. But when the summer ended, and the newly-weds discovered the incautious cedar dropped its leaves indiscriminately on to the pool-water, and cast afternoon shadows, they decided to cut the cedar-tree down; which, one day they did, without asking the old fellow's permission, and he sank to the ground with a terrible creaking and groaning sound, as if he was giving up his tree-spirit against the will of God. Ratty was terribly upset, he could not say anything at all, as this was surely not remotely 'a bit of orlright' by his book, and Old Owl, mercifully, transported him on his great safe shoulders to the cathedral of Runcton Woods. And that is where they first bumped into Winston the Urban Fox, for by then the summer had virtually ended, and, instead of being wet and draughty, turned out to be warm and windless, almost unusually so, although nobody in either the human or the animal world thought to complain, for it truly was, in Ratty's immortal phrase, 'Nice weather for the time of year'. Even Ralph the Forester had noticed something unusual earlier in the year, when a 'blackthorn winter' had carried right through until May.

Winston the Urban Fox could hear a watch ticking from fifty paces, and on a keen frosty night he was able to listen to the heart of a man beating, if he was standing still, at a hundred yards. For all its safety, he was ill at ease in the forest hiding-places, and sometimes he craved the excitement of big-city life. And its danger. He had been born some years before in a corner of Brunswick Park, which lies evenly placed between Peckham and Camberwell, and he had never entirely lost the taste for tension and furtive behaviour. It was to this London park the black people used to come in the summer of that very year when he was born, and they would spread picnics on the grass, and, as evening came, sing, and clap their hands, and exchange wonderful stories without an ending, which Winston and his family would listen to from their hiding-places. And the easy-going rhythms of hip-hop and rap, which the children used to exchange amid their ball-games, entered his head with the same intoxication as the smells of rotten hamburgers stuffed into the litter-bins along with discarded hot-dogs, and samozas. When his mother moved the litter overnight to Green Park, as they were going up in the world, he missed the endless noise and friendly banter; but the tuneful accents and jargon of those days had invaded his bloodstream, and the taste for hip-hop followed him to the royal park, with its strange, exciting international community. Now there were brass bands to enjoy every afternoon, and each morning the spectacle of the Horse Guards riding by, their breast-plates glittering in the sunshine; and colonies of hippies and Buddhists with their curious music, students with solitary clarinets and meths drinkers with mouth-organs. But it was not the same. He was nostalgic for the Caribbean sounds of 'No woman no cry', and 'Lively up Yourself', and the sweet sounds of Trench Town, Jamaica, and the Rastamen.

Late at night, after everybody but the worst reveller had caught the last tube train home, Winston would set out alone to forage and rootle among the garbage as far afield as Floral Street – even outside the very door of Fox's, the Theatrical Outfitters; and occasionally a refugee from a late-night waterhole, or club-servant returning in the early hours from the Garrick, would shake his head in disbelief to see a fox, as calm as you please, strolling down the street, rolling his tongue around his whiskers after ravaging the dustbins at Rules or Boulestin. But Winston's mother tired of city life, and the problems of traffic, which never seemed to improve, got worse in fact, and then there were the additional anxieties of pollution and poisoning. She led them, voyaging always at night and keeping secret the days, fugitive against every creature except the bat and the owl, until they reached the safety of the Sussex Downs, and the security of Runcton Woods. Where they met Old Owl and Ratty, who had recently escaped from the cedar-tree. 'Let's get together and feel all right,' said the Urban Fox, with a little skip and trot of his back-legs to brighten himself up. Owl looked upward at the canopy of thickset branches above his feathered head. 'Thorns shall come up in her palaces, and nettles and brambles in the fortresses thereof,' quoted Old Owl sagely. 'This shall be a habitation for dragons,' and he indicated, with his wing, the Urban Fox, and Ratty, together, 'and a court for owls, and they shall find a place of rest.' And Ratty contentedly muttered to them all: 'Nice weather for the time of year.'

II

RALPH the Forester walked by in the morning before even the birds were properly awake. And, as he walked, he sang softly to himself this old countryman's song.

> 'I sowed the seeds of love,
> It was all in the spring,
> In April, May, and sunny June,
> When small birds sweetly si-ing,
> When small birds sweetly sing.'

The tomatoes in Ralph's back-garden were ridged and cracked as if they were smiling. Cobwebs wound themselves round the disused drills and mowing-machines in the back shed, and acorns and horse-chestnuts ripened, polished and fell. Winston the Urban Fox made his offensives into Regnum to ransack the garbage-bins earlier each evening, the streets of the city were silent and deserted. This was the way he preferred it, and if he was lucky he

might find the occasional untended chicken, or bantam, left out of its coop by a careless housewife. It was the autumn now, and there were leatherjackets on the window and huge spiders in the bath. Golden light from the sea, silvery at its edges, and bright without any heat, danced across the fading book-jackets in the old dowager's library, catching the fine threads of cobweb which had just fastened across them like an imperceptible frost. Her croquet mallets stood idle in the hall porch, and pale sun brought out the wasp to die upon the window pane. But, deep in the shadows of Runcton Woods, Owl was as taciturn as ever. It was hushed and mild in the cedar-tree, and, spreadeagled beside his friend, Ratty would only reply when asked: 'Now this *is* a bit of orlright.' That same night, the bells in Boxgrove Priory began to ring gently, unaided by any human hand.

Could they have known it, everything was far from all right, and the first to remark on it, before even Ralph the Forester, was the Urban Fox. 'Keep on moving, and lively up yourself,' he was heard to complain, his tongue hanging out, panting eagerly. 'I'm telling you, monsters, it's evil out there . . .' And so it was. The park roses suddenly and inexplicably blossomed again, the chutney tomatoes in the allotments ripened overnight, and the creamy magnolia which grew on the back wall of the Bishop's Palace broke out into a second glorious display of waxy flowers. It was all most unusual, and everybody busily running about his business in the big city was perspiring, bad-tempered, and short of breath. From nowhere, there had come an oppressive and unaccountable summerlike heat, as if June was ready to flower all over again, in October. Nobody had ever known anything like it before; the birds began nesting, and Winston could plainly hear an amorous vixen whistling and yelping for a mate. Old Owl kept his counsel and paid no heed to the Urban Fox's plea to 'lively up yourself', although beneath his unruffled feathers, and his discreetly closed eyes, he was thinking – well, not furiously, because owls never do anything furiously, but he was thinking with meticulous care. Something in the natural world was up, he decided. It was no use discussing matters of this importance with Ratty, because, although Winston urged him to stay cool, all you could get out of him was: 'Nice weather for the time of year.' And Owl was not convinced that it was.

None of the inhabitants of Runcton Woods, in the animal kingdom or the human one, not Old Owl, with his gift for prophecy and ear for catastrophe, nor Ralph the Forester, in his white beard and brown gaiters, could have dreamed such a terrible upheaval as the one that began that night. At first, the wind began stealthily, sending a shiver across the waterways and ripes, like rubbing the fur of a cat's back the wrong way; then there was a whisper along the grasses of Starveacre Copse; then a rattle, nothing more, at the window-panes; then a flapping round the back, which made the outside door slam with a bang, and blew out the bed-sheets on the line like a yacht's spinnaker, so that Ralph the Forester put aside his pipe and newspaper and muttered: 'Best I were to see to those chicken huts!' And Mrs Ralph bustled out with a trug to 'gather the washing in'. Ratty clung contentedly to the swaying branch, enjoying the ride as if on a round-about. Old Owl, eyes cheerfully closed, because he liked the sound of the October music, heard from far away the draughts moaning among the chimney-stacks, like a fanfare of trumpets. And then, more cunningly, when in the vaulty forest the same winds soughed in the top branches, Owl was pleasantly reminded of the sweetness of strings. And that was all. When the elements roared out with the full throat of thunder, and gale piled up on gale, men thought the end of the world had come at last. The storm was as angry as a battle. Winston scuttled for shelter in a shop-door after he had been pursued by a battery of empty milk bottles, careering after him down South Street and smashing themselves against the wall. Tiles spun off the roofs in every direction, and appeared to be aimed personally at him; when he sheltered in doorways, it was no good, for shop windows exploded behind him; and, particularly hazardous, litter-bins careered towards his hide-out. Worst of all, an entire bus shelter, ripped from its moorings, cart-wheeled across the road. All over the Sussex Wild, windmills were uprooted, and crushed into pieces, their sails spin-ning down the hillsides. A circus Big Top was blown up into the air never to be seen again; it exploded, sightseers told afterwards, exactly like a paper-bag; the Cathedral at Regnum scattered tiles, stained-glass, parapets and gargoyles; and, in the country-side, the smaller churches lost their lead roofs which were peeled off like the lids of tinned sardines. At Wildernesse, the swimming-pool turned into a water-spout. In Batchmere, the greenhouses were smashed to smithereens, and three hundred tropical butterflies escaped through the holes only to perish in the Great Storm, like so many shipwrecked sailors. The Poor House lost all its windows in a single gust, an entire crop of Ribstone Pippins fell to the grass in one mighty puff, and an old dosser sheltering under a tree in King's Walk was crushed when it tumbled on top of him; a stack of chimneys collapsed in the great Tudor house of Maudlin, and in front of it, for three miles, its magnificent drive of coach-age oaks pitched forward. The family chapel was a graveyard for uprooted trees, the fourteen-hundred-year-old yew tree, under which the poet Blake had once found refuge from the rain, toppled over, and saddest of all, the mulberry tree, crippled and sprawling as it was, and planted by King Charles's own hand, crashed to the earth with a terrible groan, and lay in splinters, its foliage draped over it like a funeral wreath. And as if in an act of divine vengeance, when the tempest reached its peak, the roof of the chapel itself, where the old dowager's ancestors had worshipped for gener-ations, and where Ralph the Forester and Mrs

Ralph kept their regular pew, was rolled up as simply as a sheet of parchment.

And in the forest, as was to be imagined, the devastation was at its worst, worse than in the towns, even than in the great country-houses and gardens; because, whereas the man-made world might be rebuilt and repaired, nothing could restore the waste of wild estates which had taken perhaps a thousand years to construct and enrich. A solitary bluebell wood is the work of centuries. It was in the Sussex Wild that the very heart of the countryside was ripped out and laid bare, and punished and crushed to its deepest root; as if the elements themselves had taken control and brutally disfigured earth's countenance for ever. Entire forests snapped off like so many matchsticks, and the night air was pulpy with the biting smell of tree-sap. There were places of the forest where one tree would take revenge upon another by falling prostrate across it, as if dragging it down with itself out of spite. Pollard willows drowned in the very streams which re-freshed them; time-worn sycamores, giant horn-beams, the great forefathers of the English forests bearing ancient names, lime, Lombardy poplar, sweet chestnut, copper-beech, and silver-birch, all disgorged from the fresh earth, upturned, and left in untidy heaps. Slain like Absalom. The earth in neighbouring fields had been torn up, and whirled about, as if some giant farmer had stealthily ploughed it overnight. Birds desperate to escape were snatched out of the sky by the same giant hand,

and cattle were sucked up into it – a black-and-white cow was discovered on the topmost branches of a holm-oak; ships at anchor were driven on shore as detritus, and greenhouses and garden-sheds swept out to sea; fishes were sucked from it, and spewed over the fields, and the lighthouse which warned sailors of the treacherous Bognor Rocks simply slipped into the waves, and not a stone of it was ever seen again, as if it had never existed.

'Man – I am totally distressed and enduring harassment in this Great Blow . . .!' complained the Urban Fox to himself, dodging the tiles and slates which cascaded around his head – 'This here is Babylon to the left of I, and Babylon to the right of I!'

More trash-cans and milk bottles exploded about him. 'You have to dead to enjoy this . . .' And remembering his mother's advice, to keep your head down in a crisis, he wedged his body between gravestones in the old burial ground in the Cathedral, known as Paradise. But he never lost his optimism . . .

'Good *must* over evil,' he reminded himself, having been brought up in good Baptist faith in Brunswick Park. 'Hang in, and hold tight . . .' And a neon-sign from the Chinese Take-Away splintered on the paving stones right in front of him.

When the skreeking wind at last abated, at first light, Old Owl placed Ratty securely between his broad, safe shoulders, and, beak and ears horned into the very teeth of the storm, on strong wings

sought sanctuary in Regnum itself. And it was with no little irony – upon their safe arrival at the boughs of a tough old yew tree, which had stood guard outside the Cathedral for centuries, and had withstood many changes of years and government, and religion – that Ratty murmured: 'Nice weather for the time of year . . .'

And there they remained, while the business of clearing up the city and countryside went on, to the apprehension of the Dean and Chapter, and to the wonderment of the local congregation, who saw, after Sung Eucharist that first Sunday, sitting on one of the boughs of the churchyard yew tree, a giant eagle-owl. In the shadow of the Cathedral spire, the yew was bounded on the other side by the backs of a row of houses, and Ratty was ravished by the spicy smells from the Pizzeria and the Tandoori Restaurant. The two exhausted friends rested until the storm had blown itself out, and the long work of sweeping up the littered streets and broken shop-windows took place. Sadly, however, in Runcton Woods, stricken trees by their thousands, their tens of thousands, lay on their faces in tidy rows – like lines of soldiers, sleeping after a long march.

That same day – although the wind chilled the parishioners kneeling for Evensong, as it howled through the empty panes of stained-glass – towards evening, when darkness came, Old Owl heard the gentle, but unmistakable, harmonies of a Motet by Thomas Tallis. After the Great Blow, its sorrowful cadences filled him with such repose, that he felt he had never experienced anything so beautiful in all his life. In fact he could not remember anything quite to compare with it; not even when he was listening to the exaltation of the larks on top of the Downs, or the nightingales in Starveacre, repeating and repeating that curious hollow sound of water flowing through pipes they imitate so accurately. Sometimes high childish trebles would detach themselves from the general harmony, and wander about on their own, tracing the most eloquent of arabesques, like butterflies. It was as effortless and airy as flying. Like a tide in full flood, great waves of concord and counterpoint would float across the decorative tracery of the Cathedral beyond the carved corbels, out of the windows, until the sound ascended to the branch on which Owl was perched with Ratty beside him. And even the Urban Fox, quivering behind the stones of Paradise, felt reassured by the sound – although it was not really his kind of music. The solitary childlike high voice, calling, calling, calling, for its lost soul – and the other voices below, answering, answering, answering. Old Owl felt were he to die at that moment he could not be more happy. He thought perhaps he had died already and awoken and found himself in heaven.

Hardly daring to break the spell of such rapture, he whispered to Ratty: 'What do you make of this heavenly music, Ratty? Have you ever heard anything as lovely before?'

To which Ratty as usual replied: 'Now this *is* a bit of orlright.'

For all of the month of October, while the ravages of the Great Blow were repaired, Old Owl kept vigil in his yew tree which stood beyond the far end of the Lady Chapel in the Cathedral Church of the Holy and Undivided Trinity, and daily he listened to the Order of Service, at Matins, and the Evensong, after which he would disappear on his hunting expeditions. And, when the Prebendal Boys, with Mr Fazackerley, the Master of the Choristers, marched in crocodile for Choir Practice every afternoon between 4.30 and 5.30, he would float on his great white sails, well over four feet in width, to perch on top of the Song School; and, with Ratty on his back, he would complement their efforts with strategic hoots. When Choir Practice was ended, and the singing boys trooped down, jostling and pinching one another, not behaving like choristers should at all, he would return to his place outside the Canons' Vestry and listen to them chant, oh, so confidently and well, the treacherous Anthems of Byrd, and Taverner, over which they had struggled earlier. After they had changed from their glowing bright surplices, and were back in their post-box red blazers, walking to the Old Bishop's Kitchen for tea, with young Civil, the Senior singing boy leading them, he would swoop down to sit by St Richard's Porch, curmurring his approval, and the wicked little choirboys would lift their school-caps to him, and sometimes curmur back, before Civil cuffed the backs of their heads. This persisted for a whole week, while Old Owl got acquainted with the Cathedral's mysteries and traditions. He got to know the hours of all the services, and he had his favourites among the Cathedral clergy, picking out the choristers, the Dean, the Archdeacon, for his friendship; for others, the Wandsmen, the Priest Vicar, and the Sacrist, his disapproval. On occasion he was known to swoop alarmingly, talons outstretched, head-high at those who earned his disrespect.

But his special friend of all was the old Choirmaster, Mr Fazackerley. He was a lonely man, because his wife – to whom he was greatly attached – had died when she was very young, and he had never loved anybody again, only his beautiful church-music. And often, at night, he would let himself into his beloved Cathedral with his own key, when nobody was about, and settle himself at the hundred-pipe organ (the oldest, they say, in England) and play the church music he loved so well. And Old Owl would sit as close to the windows as he could to listen to this heavenly music, blown out of the great ornamental pipes, which seemed to him even more loud and even more beautiful, if such a thing were possible; for the dear old man was playing for himself and his wife alone. And Old Owl and Ratty as well, of course, although he did not know it at the time.

But perhaps he did, because Mr Fazackerley told Ralph the Forester (who as you know told me) that

27

every evening after organ-practice he liked nothing better than to visit The Ship and Lighter in The Pallants for a pint. Rather like his great predecessor Thomas Weelkes, the Cathedral Organist in Queen Elizabeth's day, who would have been better known if only he had not got drunk so often, and particularly during High Mass.

Anyway, this particular evening there was a slight drizzle, with the pavements shining under the street lamps. Old Mr Fazackerley concluded his organ-practice, locked up the North Door which led into the Cloisters, ready for his evening pint, when he discovered an owl on the roof watching his departure.

'Good evening, my dear fellow,' he said, and the owl clucked his response.

As he struggled to put up his umbrella in the narrow passageway of St Richard's Walk, the Choirmaster heard a rhythmic beating of wings, and saw a ghostly shadow. The great eagle-owl floated above him to survey his progress up Canon Lane, perching in the branches of the elm tree which grows in the courtyard of The Chantry. Still following his path, Old Owl flapped above him, on slow and soundless wings, as the Master made his way under the Gate House, into South Street, past the Market Cross, until he scuttled down a little alleyway to find his pint prepared and waiting for him at The Ship and Lighter. After he had downed a great many more pints (like his distinguished predecessor), Mr Fazackerley weaved his way back again to East

Street, and there was Old Owl, patiently waiting upon him, exactly where he was, sitting on top of the Market Cross; and then, following his somewhat unsteady progress from Gate House to Chantry, the Master of the Choristers found his blurred direction back to St Richard's Walk, and entered his front door. To this day, however, Mr Fazackerley will swear that the eagle-owl was following his every step, and, if not exactly a guide, certainly as a friendly presence, encouraging him by his white ghostly wings, and muffled hooting, to escort him home.

One freezing cold night in early February, Mr Fazackerley had unlocked the North Door, which led directly into the Cloisters, and pinned it back, to assist one of the most venerable of the Wandsmen through into Paradise. Suddenly, with a blur of white feathers, a draught of wind, and a rhythmic hum, before anybody could slam the door shut or deflect him, the huge eagle-owl flew *in*. And nothing could persuade him to fly out again. The great bird floated along the Nave, upward and upward, mounting higher and higher, with Ratty on his powerful back, as always, until he rested on the topmost pipes of the organ, where he remained, noble and motionless, carved in stone. He then looked about him, blinking his eyes in slow-motion, and frowning his marvellous hairy brows. Around his eyes were two circles, like the rims of a large pair of spectacles. Above him rose the tall pinnacles,

fretworked and spidery, and beneath him, led by Civil, with the Clergy in procession, all the treble-boys clothed in white, clasping the fingers of one hand lightly by the other, their hair slicked down to perfection. Evensong was just about to commence. As Mr Fazackerley conducted the opening hymn, the Owl, motionless on the organ case, seemed to oversee everything, more authoritative than the Dean, and, if such a thing were possible, more senior to the Bishop, who was present in his own Cathedral, crozier in hand. It was St Oswald's Eve.

The candles guttered and smoked in the draught, and one of the choristers stifled a painful cough, when the Priest Vicar began his address. To get a better view, Old Owl drifted down from the Triforium, and alighted on the Arundel Screen, which divides the Quire from the Congregation neatly in half. There he could survey everything at his ease. The Priest Vicar began rather nervously:

'Today is the Eve of the Feast of St Oswald, who in the Middle Ages was, as I am sure you are aware, the Bishop of Worcester and later Archbishop of York . . .' And in the small silence which followed, while the Priest Vicar drew his breath, as if in approval Old Owl murmured: 'Whooo-oo-ooooo.' There was a moment's consternation, and the Dean lifted an anxious eyebrow towards the Arundel Screen. Old Owl blinked slowly in fraternity. He then tilted his head at right-angles. The congregation kept their heads bent devotedly in prayer.

The choir-boys hardly dared lift their eyes from their hymnals. The Priest Vicar tried again:

'This day, we pray for all Bishops, that they may diligently preach Thy Word, and duly administer the godly discipline thereof . . .' Old Owl pondered for a discernible second, before giving his own blessing:

'Whooo-oo-oooo . . .'

'Through Jesus Christ Our Lord' – 'Whooo-oo-ooo' – 'Amen.'

And when the choristers stood, with the lay-vicars in their Quire-stalls behind them, to sing the beautiful anthem, 'Gloria Tibi Trinitas', how could Old Owl, immediately christened with one accord, in honour of the Saint, *Oswald*, there and then, resist singing with them, selecting, always with great taste and, of course, an infallible ear, the correct intervals in the music, when the choir fell silent?

III

S O, following Evensong on his Saint's Day,
Oswald the Owl took up residence in the
parapets of the Lady Chapel with his friend Ratty.
And Winston the Urban Fox remained outside in
Paradise, and the good Bishop and the kindly Dean
gave them Sanctuary, which is traditionally the
blessing and gift of the Church at all times to provide
refuge for the creatures of God. But dissent echoed
in the Cloisters. 'I can only express the hope my
wife does not hear the baleful creature,' said the
Sacrist to the Chief Verger, one morning after the
Eucharist. The Sacrist's wife was frequently greeted
with ill-health. Of course, there was heated discussion about it in The Residentiary at the next
meeting of Dean and Chapter. 'Well, what's to be
done about this business, Dean?' queried
Sergeant-Major Bell (known to the wicked Prebendal boys as Ding-Dong) who was Head-Verger,
and as a former Coldstreamer a splendid man for
cathedral discipline. 'There's a ruddy great owl in

the Triforium, a stuffed rat in the organ-loft, and a fox in Paradise.'

'Owls might have hooted in St Peter's Quire, and foxes stunk and littered in St Paul's,' muttered the Sacrist, in a voice ostensibly to himself, but loud enough to be overheard by all. Mr Fazackerley, the Master of the Choristers, and, needless to say, the treble-boys *and* the probationers, were all in favour of letting Oswald stay: 'Well, he seems to like listening to choir practice, and the boys sing all the better when Oswald's on the roof of the Choir School, and, although I can't quite explain it, he very rarely interrupts Responses in the wrong place, and even then always in tune.'

'I understand owls consistently hoot in B-flat,' said the Bishop's Chaplain, who was by way of being an ornithologist.

The Communar, mindful of lay-matters, said reasonably: 'We have never found an effective way to deal with what may be frankly called "the pigeon-problem", and I have to confess – judging by the piles of owl-pellets in the pulpit, and little skeletons of . . . – well, need I say more . . . ?'

'He's skinned the little beggars,' added the Head-Verger, indignantly, 'that's what! Skinned them right down to the bare bones.'

The Sacrist, whose mind dwelt continually on spiritual concerns, took a more severe line: 'I'm sorry, Dean, but I believe it to be very wrong. Spiritually wrong. Politically mistaken. It creates all kinds of awkward precedents. I mean, what about bats in the Belfry, rodents in the Retroquire, and . . . and . . .?'

'Cats in the Crypt?' broke in the Archdeacon, who was renowned for his turn of phrase. The Chapter smiled warmly.

'This owl is dangerous and ought to be banned from the Cathedral,' insisted the Sacrist.

'Come now,' rebuked the Chancellor, who was a great believer in extending the ecumenical movement to all creatures, 'we permit Thurible, the Cathedral cat, the run of the Transepts.'

'Seriously, Archdeacon, there is a dilemma here, you know. The Communar tells us, rightly in my view, of the owl's effective massacre of our pigeon population. May I remind us all of Aesop's celebrated moral: "What may be sport for you, is death to us . . ." Oswald's pastime, if I may say so, Dean, in terms of true Christian compassion, and so far as the pigeons are concerned, is disastrous and deathly.'

'Oswald seems perfectly reverent to me,' interrupted the Precentor. 'I shall not forget in a hurry last night's Responses. You'll recollect when I chanted "The Lord be with You", the congregation replied, "And with Thy Spirit", and Oswald added, perfectly in pitch, "Whoo-oo-ooo."'

'And,' added the Archdeacon, 'what about "Praise ye the Lord" – "Whoo-oo-oooo!" You really can't be more affirmative than that.'

The Dean and Chapter all agreed there. The Lord's name *was* praised.

'Besides,' added the Dean, 'how can we get rid of him, even if we wanted to? He's becoming something of a local celebrity. People for miles around flock to see Oswald the Owl.'

'And hear him,' added Mr Fazackerley.

'And *hear* him,' conceded the Dean. A short silence followed, during which distant motorway noises were audible beyond the Residentiary windows. The affable Chancellor, Canon Cropready, drew out his snuff-box, took a hefty pinch, snorted heartily, and wiped his nose on a spotted handkerchief, before taking his turn in the discussion: 'I observed last night that, when Sergeant-Major Bell turned out the lights, snuffed the candles, and opened the West Door at the end of the Nave, for the bird to scent fresh air, and fly out to freedom, the fact is Oswald refused to budge, and stayed resolutely where he was, up in the organ-loft.'

'He could easily be *shot*,' insisted the Sacrist. 'With a child's air-gun.'

There was an uncomfortable silence. Everyone felt the Sacrist had gone too far. The Cathedral Church was the House of God.

'It's bad luck to shoot an owl,' the Communar said. 'According to Biblical tradition, the owl is believed to be the harbinger of death and doom. It was always the case in the ancient days, and the Old Testament declares, in the Book of, I think' – said the Sacrist, with a triumphant, scholarly air – 'Leviticus, "In the Beginning owls were considered unclean".'

'They had something to do with the destruction of Babylon,' agreed the Chancellor, who did not like to be thought lacking in learning. 'Isaiah, isn't it? Thirty-four? Something about "the owl and the raven shall dwell in the ruins; and he shall stretch out upon them the line of confusion, and the stones of emptiness".'

'All of this is true,' agreed the Dean, 'but if we are to find divine guidance from Holy Scriptures let us look no farther than the Psalms, where the sorrowful King laments: "O how amiable are thy dwellings thou Lord of Hosts. Yea, the sparrow hath found her an house, and the swallow a nest where she may lay her young: even thy altars, O Lord of Hosts, my King and my God." I think, under the circumstances, we may interpret freely, for the sparrow and the swallow, a solitary eagle-owl. And, if my memory serves me well, is there not an ancient Spanish legend which tells us the owl is the sweetest of singers, because it was present when Jesus died upon the cross, since when it has ever shunned the daylight, and the Day of the Lord is Darkness, not Light.' And there the matter ended.

Now . . . Ralph the Forester told me one night, when he was studiously carving thatching-pegs from wattle sticks, a very dramatic event took place. The very next day, following the meeting of the Dean and Chapter, being the second Thursday of the month, was also the appointed gathering of the Diocesan Clergy Wives. They assembled together in the Bishop's Kitchen, in the Bishop's Palace, and they were being given a lecture by the Bishop's Wife. The hammer-beam rafters were high, and a great log-fire roasted in the hearth of the magnificent medieval kitchen, where in ancient days St Richard and his clerks sat behind a refectory table as heavy as an iron-roller, and as long as a cricket-pitch. The Diocesan Clergy Wives seemed to hang devotedly on every syllable which the Bishop's good lady spoke. For Mrs Fruitnight always chose this second Thursday to lecture to them about the West Sussex Saints. Not for the first time, nor the last time, either, as there seemed to be so many hundreds of them. She had just finished the story of St Cuthman, who wheeled his crippled mother in a handcart to Steyning, where he built the church which bears his name, when suddenly the stern figure of 'Ding-Dong' Bell, the Verger, burst in without knocking, and in a state of alarm. Behind his upraised arm, and through the open door, could be seen the scuttling figure of the Canon-in-Residence, his cassock flapping about his ankles, like a rook with its feathers blown backwards.

'Ladies, ladies, pardon my intrusion!' he cried, trying to recapture his breath at the same time as speaking.

'Great heavens, Sergeant-Major Bell,' said Mrs Fruitnight, 'what on earth has happened? You look as if you've just seen the spire collapse into the middle of the Cathedral, just as it did in the winter of 1861.' The Clergy Wives winced at the recollection.

'Oh, My Lady,' panted the Verger, uncertain in

his panic how to address a Bishop's wife, 'it's very nearly as great a catastrophe. Ladies! There's a man from the Leisure Centre come with a shrimp-net to snatch our Oswald out of the organ-loft!'

A second shiver of horror swept through the Diocesan Clergy Wives. They forgot all about the West Sussex Saints in a trice, and murmured angrily between themselves. Elegant hats swivelled back and forth; some ladies reached for umbrellas and handbags. By this time, Oswald had become something of a celebrity in his own right; he had not sought Sanctuary in vain. The idea of a dignified eagle-owl entertaining coach-parties in a Theme Park filled the Clergy Wives with dismay. At this moment, equally out of breath, the Canon-in-Residence arrived at the doorway of the Bishop's Kitchen in even – can it be imagined? – a deeper state of anxiety than the Verger.

'Dear ladies of the Diocese,' he began, 'the Dean and Chapter urgently require, no, beseech, your assistance – an employee of a most suspicious nature, armed with some kind of fishing-implement, claiming to be a representative of a wild-fowl sanctuary, is trying to extricate Oswald from his tabernacle. He is now, even as we speak, engineering his vehicle opposite the Chantry, and, if we do not move swiftly, may, I fear, apprehend him.'

'Then there is not a minute to lose,' said the Bishop's Wife, with the same resolution she had shown that afternoon when she entertained four hundred Anglican Bishops to high tea. 'Let us close ranks, and relieve Oswald of his tormentor.'

'I knew the Clergy Wives could be depended upon, bless their hearts,' said the Sergeant-Major. Their steadfastness reminded him of the Guards Division at Waterloo.

'Thank you, *thank you*, dear ladies,' said the Canon-in-Residence, with evident relief. 'The menace from the Leisure Centre is planning to invade by means of the West Alley. I feel confident we are in time to repel his advance at St Richard's Walk. But we have barely a moment to lose!'

'Now, Mrs Fruitnight, now's your time!' called out the Verger, recalling the Great Duke. And then he had to flatten himself against the porch as the Diocesan Clergy Wives stormed by him out of the kitchen, brandishing their brollies.

'Do you not think, Mrs Fruitnight,' ventured the timid wife of the Rector of Halnaker, ' a little prayer to St Richard might help the general cause?'

'This is no time for prayer, Mrs Inkpen,' stormed the Bishop's Wife, 'when Oswald is in danger – he might be abducted even now, while we are dithering about in the Kitchen on our knees! Right shoulders forward, ladies, and follow me!'

As the division of Diocesan Clergy Wives wheeled in procession from the Bishop's Kitchen, past the Treasury, and into the Cloisters, even Winston the Urban Fox took fright, and ducked behind a gravestone. Sergeant-Major Bell felt the urge to salute, and stood proudly at attention, thoughts of the Coldstream and the Château of Hougoumont not far from his mind. The Canon-in-Residence felt similar stirrings of the Church Militant and hummed under his breath the opening bars of: 'Who would true valour see, Let him come hither . . .' And, as the regiment of women rounded the corner into St Richard's Walk, where the homely saint used to meditate, and where the luckless official (who only meant kindness to poor Oswald) stood with his shrimping-net, the ranks of Clergy Wives in order of Parochial seniority descended upon him. Down the narrow pathway they came, the redoubtable Mrs Fruitnight in the van. Past the residence of Mr Fazackerley, past the archway into the Chantry, through the Theological College, where the Bursalis Prebendary and a crocodile of Wiccamical Prebends squeezed themselves against the wall, until they blocked the medieval walk between the bird-catcher and the Cathedral. As defiant as a battalion with banners, the consorts of Streatley and Goring, Colworth and Earnley, Brimfast and Bracklesham, Halnaker and Highleigh, Sizzleham and Selsea, stood their ground.

'*No pasaran!*' came the cry, instituted by Mrs Cattermole, the wife of the Vicar of Hastings who, like its electorate, held radical left-wing views. One look along the steadfast lines of the Clergy Wives, one look at the basilisk stare of Mrs Fruitnight, and the employee from the Leisure Centre fled the field and the Cloisters, abandoning his shrimping-net to seek the refuge of his Theme Park. In the annals of the Cathedral and its ancient history, apart from the day when the Romans abandoned the City Walls and Cromwell's cavalry stabled their horses in the Nave, everybody agreed the Defence of the Diocesan Clergy Wives ranked as Regnum's finest hour.

There the matter might have ended, and Oswald the Owl, to this day, would be deep in Runcton Woods, instead of living on church mice and pigeons, as he does in the lovely green stone Cathedral Church of the Holy and Undivided Trinity. However . . .

Something else happened, not very widely known, but remembered and respected by all of those who loved the protective presence of Oswald the Owl, and who loved their Cathedral. Certainly, Ralph the Forester remembers it, and he told me of that melancholy time of year, twelve days after Christmas, when the cheerful decorations are taken down and folded away, and the cards and wrinkled balloons confined to the rubbish corner. The first Sunday of Epiphany fell that year (it is still Ralph the Forester telling me) on a freezing day in January. The Cathedral was full of draughts, the choristers full of head-colds. It was not really a religious tradition, but more a tradition upheld by Mr Fazackerley, that he should play the recorder in quartet with one of the Lay-Vicars, the Chancellor, and a Junior-Canon, while the Dean and Chapter, and the Choir and children, walked in procession by candle-beam. And Regnum's greeny-grey Cathedral never looked more lovely, so Ralph said, like a great

upturned wooden ship, full of waving shadows. In this empty darkness, the silent congregation would hear from afar the faint sound of the wood-pipes. The solitary light shone dimly upon a tinsel star suspended from the Triforium on a thin wire. Beneath it, the stone altar-screen and the crib. Above them, the angels (the best-behaved of the probationers) and the trumpeters, seated out of sight.

For the Master of the Choristers, this was merely a modest act of reverence, to illustrate, as it were, the pathway of the Three Wise Men and their lonely journey from so far away. So that the Magi – who were the Lay-Vicars dressed up – walked along holding their candle-ends in darkness up the centre of the nave; and the shepherds before them (portrayed by the three smallest probationers with tea-towels around their heads, and their father's dressing-gowns and walking-sticks in hand), all bidden to the altar by the haunting sounds of the recorders. Then, the tradition was, once they had all arrived under the star, close to the crib, they would light their candle-ends from a solitary taper until the Cathedral was filled by one glorious flickering light. Then the trumpeters on top of the Arundel Screen sparkled out with a bright and glittering fanfare. That, as Ralph told me, was the plan. For, at that moment the choir would sing the great Transfiguration Anthem by Tallis:

O Nata Lux de Lumine!

45

The congregation would feel as if a sun was rising before them, right there in the middle of the Cathedral, and old Mr Fazackerley's eyes sting with tears (which he always put down apologetically to candle-smoke getting into them). This simple ceremony of shadow and candle-light had started quite spontaneously the year before the war, and only Mr Fazackerley himself could remember the time, the faces of the cloisters had so changed, but it was his proudest achievement. It meant so much to him that it went well on the night. The new Sacrist, who had ideas of his own, and indeed some of the Series Two clergy disapproved and thought it all rather 'high', and even wished to abandon it, but it was Mr Fazackerley's personal gift to the Cathedral he loved. Over the years, of course, the Master had grown old (he never seemed very young, not even when he was junior organist at the beginning), hard of hearing, rather near-sighted, and unsteady on his pins. Especially if he had visited The Ship and Lighter beforehand. This night, to give himself a little Christian courage (the event always made him nervous), he had indeed nipped in for a couple of quick halves of Old Ale, just to whet his lips, and, as he used to say, 'warm his finger-ends'. Somehow – was it the freezing fog in the cloisters, the extra darkness (for cloud had crossed the moon), or above all the pitch black inside the Cathedral? – Mr Fazackerley arrived at the Retroquire out of breath, hot and bothered and false-footed. The Retroquire, behind the high altar, was the area selected for the four musicians to meet and to play their recorders in pitch. The Lay-Vicar on the bass twanged his tuning-fork against the altar-rail, and whispered, 'Here's your B-flat, Mr Cohu,' and the Junior-Canon entered with the descant against the old Master's tenor, followed by the Chancellor on the treble. The four men were forced to stand around the solitary sheet of music, near the Lady Chapel, where they could share the flame of a solitary night-light. Just as they found the harmony, and played the fugitive air, before the Choir could join in with the Epiphany Hymn – horror upon horrors – the Churchwarden opened a side-door into the Clois-ters. A sharp draught, which had been lying in wait for such an opportunity, elbowed its way in, skipped round the base of two pillars before anyone could stop it, and *out* went the candle. The entire Ca-thedral now stood in inky blackness, as impenetrable as before the Creation of the World. The quartet of recorders, blinded before their music, dis-oriented, and out of sorts, lost their time, and slithered and stumbled into a horrendous silence.

'Oh, Mr Fazackerley,' whispered the bass-man, 'we can't see no longer to play our tune . . .'

Mr Fazackerley fumbled for his matches, but remembered he had left them behind in The Ship and Lighter next to his half-pint, and together with his breathlessness, his unsteady legs, and the effect of the beers beforehand, he felt his senses reel, his head spin, as if he were under water.

By the great West Door, the Sacrist twisted his

head slightly within its white cowl, which gave the effect of a polar bear, and lifted a supercilious eyebrow towards the Dean – but, as it was pitch-black, he could not, of course, be seen. The boy with the thurible cupped his mouth with his free hand. But just at that moment, when the terrible silence appeared to magnify itself and echo in that vast space, out of the darkness, there came . . . 'Tu-whoooo . . . ! Tu-whoooo . . . !' Oswald the Owl, from the centre of the Arundel Screen, as if hearing the distress of his dear old Master far off in the Retroquire, gave him his note, with an unerring and impeccable B-flat! The mellifluous, long-drawn-out sound floated over the top of the Arundel Screen, unhindered through the Quire Stalls, leapt above the panelling of the Retroquire, and descended, as if on soundless wings, on to the very lips of the four anxious woodwind players.

'Oswald's given us our note, boys,' breathed Mr Fazackerley with profound gratitude. 'Now we're safely back in harmony again!'

And, holding their recorders before them, the quartet walked carefully forward to their places in front of the Procession. When they reached the North Transept, where the shepherds joined them, Oswald hooted to them again, and guided their footsteps confidently to the Great West Door. There stood the Three Wise Men, and the tableau was complete. Even in the darkness, with not a candle to guide them, Oswald's carefully timed hooting led the Dean's Procession up the nave and under the Star, where lay the crib, and the Virgin and Child (represented by the Bishop's secretary, and her six-month-old baby girl) and Henry, from the donkey-sanctuary. Standing behind them, holding on to Henry, with a supply of carrots, was the Innkeeper, and the Innkeeper's Wife. This personable character was played with fervent integrity by the ten-year-old daughter of a local amateur actress, who, when asked by the Bishop what she thought the Nativity Story was all about, solemnly replied: 'Well, you see it's about this Innkeeper's Wife.'

'Tu-whoo!', magnifying the Lady Chapel. 'Tu-whooo!', resounding about the arches of the Triforium. 'Te-wit! Tu-whoooo!' re-echoing in the Arundel Screen and answering Oswald's tremulous call, up the Nave marched the four recorder-players with the Wise Men and Shepherds at their heels. Behind them, the choristers dressed in red, like strolling pillar-boxes, with white puritan collars. Then came the mighty Bishop and his Chaplain and the rest of the Clergy, in their Epiphany raiment, and after them children – hundreds and hundreds, and hundreds of children, all from the West Sussex schools – even more than Mrs Fruitnight's West Sussex Saints. All bidden towards the Star which overhung the Screen, in the very centre of which perched Oswald, supremely commanding, and next to him Ratty, sprawled a little awkwardly along the parapet, but mixed up chummily with the Cherubim and Seraphim. And instead of saying, 'Now this *is* a bit of orlright,' which he should have, because it *was* a bit of all right, all he could think of was, 'Nice weather for the time of year!'

When the Clergy and Choir and children assembled by the crib, and faced the congregation – some on their feet by now, some on their knees – and the lost matches were found, the candles lit, the stalk of candelabrum hoisted aloft, the tinsel-star captured in an unearthly light, the assistant jubilating mightily on the four-manual organ, and the trumpeters sparkling their fanfare – the West Doors opened wide to let the spirit of the new-born Christ enter the Cathedral. And, as all eyes turned, who should dance cheekily up the centre of the Nave, hip-hopping all the way, but Winston the Urban Fox. The Thurifer almost fainted into the arms of the Bishop's Chaplain. Civil, the senior singing-boy, gulped in astonishment. Everybody stared at the single file of dainty footprints, because Winston had got his paws damp crossing the graveyard. But nobody, from Bishop to the boy bell-ringers, could resist applauding his mischievous effrontery.

And Winston too, for all of his urban upbringing, was impressed:

'There's canons to the right of I, and canons to the left of I . . .' he whispered proudly, his eyes glinting in the candle-light. Oswald puffed and huffed and fluffed up all his feathers, and opened wide his circular yellow eyes in sheer delight, and then twisted his head round two hundred and seventy degrees, to the astonishment of the congregation. And the poor little Thurifer, who had only

just recovered from seeing an Urban Fox dance up the Nave, fell back again into the arms of the Bishop's Chaplain, at the sight of an eagle-owl with its head back to front. The three Lay-Vicars, dressed in the oriental robes of the Wise Men, stepped forward before the crib; and then the poorest shepherd knelt humbly:

'Take Frankincense, O God, take Gold, O
  King,
Take Myrrh, O Man, from those who can them
  bring.
Poor I, nor Gold, nor Myrrh, nor Frankincense
Have to present, such is mine indigence . . .'

'What's *indigence*, my man?' asked Winston.
'Destitution, you fool,' whispered Oswald.
'It's a jungle out there, man,' and the Urban Fox shook his head in dismay, while the poorest shepherd continued:

'Yet will I with these noble Persians bring
Some present still, when I salute my King:
I'll give myself. A gift too vile, too base,
To be presented to so high a grace.'

Taking these words as a signal, the young children stepped forward, and some of them shyly, some boldly, and some – it must be admitted – rather reluctantly, brought forth brightly wrapped presents from behind their backs, and laid them at the foot of the crib. Soon there was a pile of exciting and tantalising packages all round the manger, although the Innkeeper's Wife was suspicious of the largest of them. She felt certain their gaudy wrappings concealed the least wanted Christmas presents.

During this part of the proceedings, while Mr Fazackerley played the Epiphany hymn, 'Brightest and best of the sons of the morning', the Urban Fox asked Oswald why these Three Wise Men had set out on so difficult a journey, and endured such hardship, just for a small child. And at such an inconvenient time of year. Surely, they would prefer to spend Christmas with their families like everybody else. Oswald the Owl, who knew the answers to almost everything, said that, although it was true the journey had been rather disagreeable, in their own country, strictly speaking, in December it was – 'Nice weather for the time of year!'

'And, after all,' continued Oswald, unconcerned, as if Ratty had not even opened his mouth, 'a great prince had bidden them.'

'Awesome,' said Winston, his eyes brightly shining. But, had the trip been worth it, he persisted, 'after all that heavy effort, man, and all that harassment'? And Oswald – who was grave in nature as well as in speech (after all, to be 'serious as an owl' is a well-known saying) – replied: 'Well, evidently, otherwise being wise, and not foolish, men, they would have given up long ago. Wouldn't they?'

'Wicked,' said Winston, and grinned his grin of

deep content, which looked to people who did not know him more like a scowl. After all, he was mindful of taking a long and fearful journey himself, years ago. And Ratty said . . . Well, that you can work out for yourself!

IV

YOU will probably want to know what happened to Oswald and his two friends from the Wild. Did they return to Runcton Woods, now the storm had subsided? Well, according to Ralph the Forester, the Urban Fox still survives among the tombstones and garbage-pails, and Ratty spends most of his day slumbering in the Arundel Screen. As for Oswald, he is such a celebrity that pilgrims now visit the Cathedral at Regnum from far and wide, in order to see him. And you can see him there for yourself, if you wish. But you have to be up early in time for Mattins, or have finished your tea, in good time for Evensong. Because, any later than that, you see, he goes off on his hunting expeditions. And if the naughty Prebendal boys lower their voices, out of mischief, to sing a G-major chord, you may hear him too. Because he sits joyfully on the organ-case, listening to the Sacred Music of those old Tudor composers he loves so well: the ancient and serene harmonies of Thomas Tallis and 'that common drunkard' Thomas Weelkes; and Orlando Gibbons and John Taverner; and the anthems and canticles and motets and madrigals of John Bull and William Byrd, a perfect singing of God's praises, day by day, in the Sarum Rite, which is church music at its very best. As the good Dean said, after a particularly rousing Hymn for the Transfiguration, 'the heavenly harmony allows us one more glimpse of the face of God'.

But Oswald also likes just as much the grumpy Victorian hymns, with their familiar titles, The Old Hundredth, The Old Hundred and Fourth, Ravenscroft, Bishop Ken, Old Martyrs, and, of course, Oswald's Tree – and then there are the tunes for Sunday services which go by the names of suburban railway stations: Totteridge, Barnet, and Royal Oak, East Peckham, Ivy Hatch, and Poplar. And, whenever it comes up in the hymnal, he always croons his approval of St Oswald's triumphant 'Through the night of doubt and sorrow, onward goes the pilgrim band', because he naturally enjoys anything which has an 'o' or an 'ooo' in it. And he always has a soft spot in his heart for Cardinal Newman's sorrowful song:

> Lead kindly light
>   Amid the encircling gloom,
> Lead thou me on,
> The night is dark,
>   And I am far from home . . .

for he remembers the Great October Blow, when the encircling gloom was all about them, as he flew with Ratty on his shoulders from Runcton Woods, and *they* were far from home, and he, Oswald the Owl, was the kindly light, leading them on. Best of all, he loves Advent, and the end of November, and the end of another year, when the evenings grow dark in the middle of the day, and Wandsmen extinguish the electric chandelier, and light with a long taper the rush candle-beam. Ah! Then the Cathedral looks like a great upturned ship, shadowy and mysterious as a forest, smelling of tallow-wax and fragrant cedar-wood. While the baritones and tenors of the Lay-Vicars sing the lower line, and the boy-trebles take the top line, Oswald – sitting above them in the middle of the Arundel Screen, presiding over the service with the eminence of an Archbishop – joins in the majestic Advent Anti-phons. Now, in the dormitories of the Prebendal, the wicked little Choristers used to call these Antiphons, with their sonorous Latin phrases 'O Sapientia', 'O Emmanuel', 'O Radix Jesse', 'the Great O's' – but after Oswald had sung his part in them, they re-christened them 'the Great Oooo's', and every-body agrees his contribution is nothing if not mel-lifluous. He never sings out of tune, and never seems to enter on the wrong beat. Of course, his taste is extremely conservative, and he does not approve of dissonance in the canticles, when he snaps his beak, and ruffles his feathers. He also takes great exception to the Alternative Version of

the Nunc Dimittis in which the Synod replaced 'thee' by 'you-ooo', even if it is easier for him to sing.

Most of the day, Oswald perches on the Arundel Screen, and sometimes above the organ-case, and sometimes he disappears into the Lady Chapel for hours of meditation (or is it mice?). But there are other times, when Oswald imperially takes off, and, soaring up as high as the topmost pinnacles, he floats on extended wings the entire length of the Nave, from Triforium to Retroquire and back again, with a great sweeping sound. And then there are quieter times, when there are only the choirboys practising in the Quire-stalls, and Oswald perches just inside the Clerestory windows of the Lady Chapel, looking out from his beloved Cathedral towards Paradise where his friend, Winston the Urban Fox, lies snugly among the gravestones. And when the choir sing out rapturously: 'Blow up the Trumpet in the New Moon', Ratty mutters: 'Nice weather for the time of year!'

And when the treble-boys nearly burst out of their surplices to cry:

'Sing we merrily unto God our strength:
Make a cheerful noise unto the God of Jacob . . .

Ratty sighs contentedly,   'Now this *is* a bit of orlright!'